Where Golfers Buy Their Pants

Where Golfers Buy Their Pants
And Other Collected Cartoons

Sports Cartoons by

STEVE MOORE

MACMILLAN • USA

Macmillan Publishing Company
15 Columbus Circle
New York, NY 10023

MACMILLAN is a registered trademark of Macmillan, Inc.

Library of Congress Cataloging-in-Publication Data
Moore, Steve.
    Where golfers buy their pants and other collected cartoons /
    Steve Moore. — 1st ed.
        p.   cm.
    ISBN 0-02-035127-5
    1. Golf—Caricatures and cartoons.   2. American wit and
    humor, Pictorial.   I. Title.
    NC1429.M727A4   1994
    741.5'973—dc20   94-593   CIP

10   9   8   7   6   5   4   3   2   1

Printed in the United States of America

To my mom

"Whoa, whoa, whoa! What, are you crazy, Leonard? You'll get cramps. Wait 20 minutes to digest before you go in the water."

"Well, we're doomed. They didn't see us, and that was our last flare."

"Back off, Fred, you heard him wrong. He said you have a really big putt."

"Surrounded by munchkins on the first tee, attacked by flying monkeys on the seventh, now this ... I say we skip the back nine, Herb."

8

"How many times did I warn you, Frank? How many times? I said stay away from the roughs, Frank."

"Crud! Wouldn't you know it. Right into a land hazard ..."

"I need a new golf cart ... And you might want
to send a doctor out to the 9th green."

12

"Bob, you run back to the clubhouse and call their wives. I'll try to find us another twosome."

"I said hand me the *putter*."

Dr. Feldman's fall from grace was swift and he was inevitably branded a heretic and shunned by his peers in the medical community.

"Ha! Right smack in the middle of a grass trap!!"

The deadly Venus Golfer Trap

9-19

"Excuse me, Mr. Oliver, but there are two gentlemen here who would like to play through..."

12-7

" ... Aah, aah *SHANK IT!* ... Whoa, excuse me ... *SHANK IT!* ... hoo, must be an allergy ... aah, aah, aaaah *SHANK IT!!* ... sorry ... "

17

"OK, I think I understand: Head down. Slow backswing. Then just barely knick the ball so it only travels about five feet."

"It's working ... "

19

"Goodbye, dear. Have a good game."

" ... OK, OK, Bob. I promise to keep quiet while you're trying to putt ... Bob? Joke's over, Bob ... Bob??"

"Hey, Bob ... what does this word mean:
'Skeletonize'?"

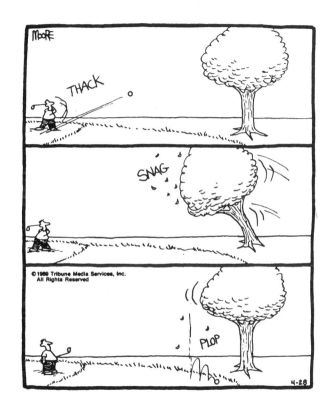

Synchronized golfing

23

" ... Well, I guess it was about, oh, a hundred-yard shot over a sand trap, and ... Hey Earl! Did I nail him with a seven or eight iron?"

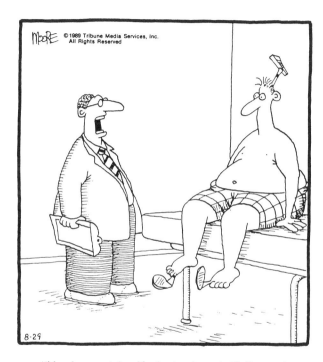

"You've got 'golfer's toe' and, if I'm not mistaken, early symptoms of 'golf on the brain' ... "

Golf course gridlock

Every spring the golfers are flushed from the fairways
and into nets where they are tagged and released
relatively unharmed.

"Keep it up, Floyd ...scream and yell ... we'll see how you like it when you're trying to concentrate ... "

Where golfers buy their pants.

"Now, I'll ask you again ... mind if we play through?"

" ... So then Larry hits his tee shot, and the ball
... Dang! Larry, I forget, is it a 'hook' or a 'slice'
when the ball sails off to the right?"

" ... Wait, here it is. 'The other members of the foursome may either dislodge the player or take a penalty stroke and continue without him' ..."

"Yo!! Mind if we play through?"

"I think you'd better drive the cart."

"Look, don't worry about it, Bob. I mean, if they live in a house next to a fairway they've got to expect occasional damage from errant golf balls ..."

"Four!!"

Pinocchio takes up golf

"Wow. Poor Dewey. Engulfed in a celestial vortex and sucked from the face of the Earth ... dibs on his clubs!"

"Golfers! Quick, hide the tasteful stuff!!"

"Hop out. Your ball landed right about here."

"I hate the first tee. I always feel so self-conscious, like my every move is being watched."

"Yo! ... Need a fourth?"

"Hop on. They were out of carts."

The Putter of Excalibur

"... A great guy, a loving husband and, uh,
we're-really-going-to-miss-him-amen   ...
OK, let's putt out. The foursome behind us is
waiting to tee off."

PGA officials later reversed themselves and rescinded the decision to allow heckling at tournaments.

"Look, Bob, maybe you should just play another ball."

"Never fails ... always just as I'm about to putt."

"There's my ball. Stay in the cart, Floyd."

"Hurry. She's starting to come to."

"Thank God! Kenny! Someone's spotted us!!"

Sister Mary Francis salvages a par.

"Well shoot, Ted. Here's why you're not getting any distance... You're suppose to take that little sock thingy off the head of your club."

" ... OK, OK, OK, OK!! You can play through!!!"

"You must have sunk it. Dewey's screaming."

"You think we should report this to the pro shop?"

"Listen carefully, Don. Run to the clubhouse, explain what happened to Bob and get back here pronto. There's a foursome behind us waiting to tee off."

Golf defined

Stationary golf cart: All the aerobic benfits of riding around for 18 holes, but in the privacy of your home or office!

"Whoa, that's a nasty hook you've got there, Doug. Try moving farther back in the seat and straighten your left elbow."

Getting in shape with golf

Step aerobics for golfers

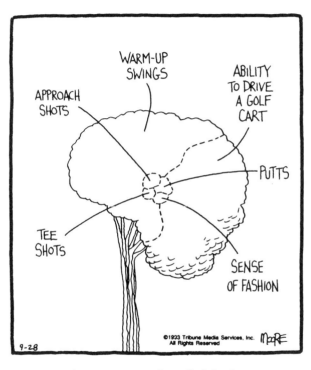

Control centers of a golfer's brain

"Wait! He didn't win, majesty. I added wrong. You actually won by a stroke."

"We found the groaning noise, Mrs. Lieberman. Your husband was lodged under the axle."

58

"Uh, uh, uh ... you're coming dangerously close to being audible, Mr. Koss. Whisper, Mr. Koss. This isn't a hockey game."

"Gosh, dad, Richy and I were just tearing apart a golf ball to see what was inside ..."

"I'm serious, Wayne. I really think that, just this
once, you should go back and replace your divot."

"Take cover ..."

"Go ahead and putt. He just said his ball rolled over the edge of the yeeeaaaah ..."

"I did it, I did it! A once-in-a-lifetime hole in one! And thank goodness you're here as a witness, Bob!!"

Fall from Eden: the untold story

"The heck with it. You want to go play some tennis?"

"OK, now this next hole goes straight for about 100 yards, then angles off in the shape of a you-know-what leg ..."

"Beautiful drive, Bob ... You were supposed to tee off in the other direction, though ...

"Joe, you fool, replace your divot!"

"I think he's trying to tell us something. Yo,
Bob! If you've thrown your back out,
blink three times!"

"I don't like the foursome you put me with."

Roy eventually found his ball, but soon realized that perhaps he had wandered too far into the rough.

"Did you see where it landed, Roy?"

"... But wait, Bob, here's some good news. According to this, you'll only be **assessed a one-stroke penalty.**"

"You've got to ease up on your backswing, Roy."

Life 101

Wolves in the rough

"Well, it's definitely some kind of creature, but I'd say it's only about twice the size of a golf cart."

Hustler preying upon the fashion-impaired.

Golf balls for brains

74

Futile attempts

"You're right, Dick, it does look like Armageddan ... WAAAH! Did you see that?! I sank a chip shot! I sank a chip shot!!"

"Don't be a fool, Andy. Let them play through."

The truth about water hazards

"That was pretty good ... you kept your eyes on the ball. Head down. Nice follow-through ... now let's work on your grip."

"It'll probably break toward the water."

"Whoa, whoa, whoa! What are you forgetting, Larry? I can't believe you were going to just walk away without replacing your divot."

Funeral for a golfer

"Whoa, bummer. Close, but no cigar. You don't get in ... next!!"

Further evidence that God is into golf

"Keep it up, Ethel. You can make deep, threatening guttural sounds until you're blue in the face. I'm not going to let it ruin my game."

Robert was not very good, but loved the excercise and
opportunity to network.

"Oh, no you don't, Floyd! March right back in here
and replace your divot!!"

"We ventured off the designated cart path."

"Now don't panic ... I'll go phone his wife. You stay here and figure out why your shots keep veering off so sharply ... "

Assorted hooligans

Arnold Palmer as a kid

"Bummer about your back, Andy. Don't move. Paramedics will be here soon. Meanwhile, let's say – God forbid – your back is history. No more golf. I'm just talking worst case, OK? ... Can I have your clubs, Andy?"

"Just swat it away, Alice. This is a golf course. There's bound to be insects."

The tournament is posponed as golfballs the size of hail begin to fall.

Miracle of the hooks and slices

Cypress Sholes Country Club and Crocodile Reserve

Steve Moore, who began cartooning at age fourteen in his eighth-grade English textbook, lives in Marina Del Rey, California. When he is not holding down the news editor's desk at the *Los Angeles Times,* Steve gets many of his best ideas for his cartoons while stuck in Southern California freeway traffic. His first two collections of sports cartoons, *Born in the Bleachers* and *Revolution in the Bleachers,* provided many laughs for sports fans. Steve's nationally syndicated strip, "In The Bleachers," is carried by Tribune Media Services in more than 200 newspapers daily.